The Monster on the ...

Written by Becca Heddle

Illustrated by Omar Aranda

Collins

We are waiting for a train in the gloom.
I scoop up my trailing scarf.

Scanning the tracks, I spot a flash of bright green near the platform.

The train appears. A bright green monster creeps on to the train.

Screech!

4

The green monster frowns and growls.
It slinks along the train.

I trail along too.

The monster grabs some burnt toast.
It sinks its pointed teeth into it.

Crunch!

The monster drops the toast crusts.
I clear them up with a broom.

It drains three cans of brown drink.
The drink spurts and stains my coat.

The monster scrubs my coat with my scarf. The stain disappears.

The monster grins. It grabs a flower for me, then starts to flee.

Thank you!

It clambers up the steep ladder to the train roof.

It runs along the train.

The monster jumps into the trees.
Its fur floats in the wind.

Is the monster asleep now, by the train tracks? Sleep tight, monster.

Monster on the tracks

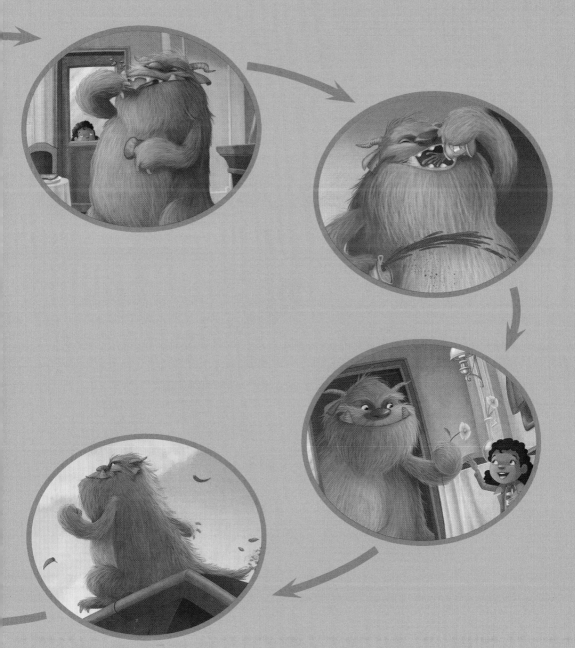

 Review: After reading

Use your assessment from hearing the children read to choose any GPCs, words or tricky words that need additional practice.

Read 1: Decoding
- Model reading words with adjacent consonants and long vowel sounds. Take the word, **brown**. Say each of the sounds quickly and clearly, b/r/ow/n. Then blend the sounds together. Ask the children to do the same.
- Now ask the children to sound out and blend the following words:
  pointed   monster   bright   screech

Read 2: Prosody
- Choose two double page spreads and model reading with expression to the children.
- Ask the children to have a go at reading the same pages with expression.

Read 3: Comprehension
- Turn to pages 14 and 15 and recap the story of the monster on the train.
- For every question ask the children how they know the answer. Ask:
  - Before she gets on the train, what does the girl spot on the platform? (*bright green fur*)
  - What does she do when the monster drops his toast crusts? (*she sweeps them up*)
  - Do you think the girl likes the monster? Why or why not?
  - Do you think the girl tells her mum about the monster? Why or why not?